The Abou Abed

كتابـــ نكاتـــ أبو عبد ❷

Compiled by: Sabina Mahfoud
Illustrated by: Daniel Georges
Edited by: Abed Al-Mawla, Tarek Ballout, Claude Karam
Designed by: Maya Tawil

turning**point**
B O O K S

15th Floor, Concorde Building, Dunan Street, Verdun, Beirut, Lebanon
P.O. Box: 14 - 6613
Tel: 00 961 1 752 100
Fax: 00 961 1 748 555
www.tpbooksonline.com

First edition: December 2009

ISBN: 978-9953-0-1583-5
Printing: **dots**

To Abou Tara and Abou William

As Abou Abed belongs to the Lebanese, part of the proceeds from this book will be donated to the Lebanese non-profit organization CIFA (Centre d'Insertion par la Formation et l'Activité) to support sustainable development projects throughout Lebanon.

INTRODUCTION

When *The Abou Abed Joke Book* was released in 2008 many Lebanese were surprised. Why on earth didn't anyone bring out such a book earlier, was a common question posed to me. It was received so well that I decided to go ahead and bring out a second volume; this time Abou Abed has been brought to life by the talented illustrator Daniel Georges.

Who is Abou Abed? Here is a short introduction: With his red tarbouche hat and considerable moustache, a symbol of his virility, Abou Abed is one of the most recognizable comic characters in Lebanon. A figment of our imagination, he has evolved to almost celebrity status and is at the center of hundreds of jokes. He spends his time with his friend Abou Steif in a Beirut coffee shop where they play cards and backgammon. Over endless cups of tea they tell each other far-fetched stories, usually orientated around their sexual potency. Not very well off, he regularly tries his luck with card games and the lottery.

Abou Abed is married to Em Abed (literally mother of Abed) and has a son called Abed; they bear the butt of his jokes but sometimes manage to turn the tables back on him. We are always left guessing as to his profession and sexual orientation - he never seems to be working and he is game for anything.

My fascination with Abou Abed began many years ago, during Lebanon's Civil War, when, many of us were forced to stay close to home for long stretches of time. Evenings were spent with family and neighbors, telling Abou Abed jokes to forget the tensions; my husband, especially, is renowned for his incredible repertoire and elaborate renditions.

A few years ago I started to write down from memory some of the jokes, and the idea of publishing a book to introduce Lebanon's best loved comic character to a wider audience came to mind.

Some of you are sure to dwell on my choice of jokes and may be disappointed about not seeing your favorite here. Those of you familiar with Abou Abed's character will know that some of his best stories are spicy X-rated and I could not put them on paper.

In my opinion, Abou Abed belongs to a utopian age where the average Lebanese had no real problems and all a man needed to worry about was how to have a good time with his friends. He represents the ordinary Lebanese guy with all of his flaws, but also his greatness - in this case an exceptional sense of humor. Although his stories cheer us up I have often wondered how Abou Abed can get away with being such a chauvinist bigot - and come out on top looking like a working-class hero!

So where is he now? Abou Abed seems to be eternal and a survivor - he lives on with each and every generation in Lebanon. As a character, he may leave much to be desired, but as long as the jokes keep rolling in, who cares. Let's keep on searching and let me know when you find him as I would love to hear his stories first-hand!

Sabina, Beirut, December 2009.

أبو العبد رجع من أميركا، مبسوط. كتير بالسفرة. قلو لأبو صطيف «مش معقولين الأميركان شو مهذبين ومحترمين، وبحبّو كل الأديان والأنبياء، تصوّر أنو كل نبي في مدينة باسمو: سان فرانسيسكو، سان دييغو، سان خوسيه، حتى أنا حبّوني كتير وسمّوني «سان أوف أيه بيتش.»

Abou Abed returned from his holiday in the United States. Enthusiastically, he told his friends all about the wonderful trip to California. "Americans are so friendly and so religious - they give all their cities names of saints: San Francisco, San Diego, San Jose. And they liked me so much that they gave me a saint's name too. They called me 'San Ofabitch'."

أبو العبد وأبو صطيف قاعدين بالقهوة عم يتحدثو، «ابو العبد، شو رح تعمل لمرتك بمناسبة عيد زواجكم الـ25؟» سألو أبو صطيف. «والله عم فكر آخدها على استراليا» جاوب ابو العبد. «واو كتير منيح، طيب وبمناسبة عيد زواجكم الـ50 شو حتعمل يا ابو العبد؟» ردّ أبو العبد «بإذن الله برجّعها من أستراليا على لبنان!»

Abou Abed and Abou Steif were sitting in their favorite café discussing Abou Abed's upcoming 25th wedding anniversary. "What are you going to get Em Abed?" asked Abou Steif. "Well I am thinking of taking her to Australia."

"That's really generous. But, what will you do for her on your 50th anniversary then?" asked Abou Steif. "Well, I will go to Australia and bring her back to Lebanon!" replied Abou Abed.

إجا أبو العبد عند دكتور نفساني وخبره أنّو دائما بيتخيل نفسه
كلب أبيض كبير، حتى أنّو أوقات بعوّي.
قلو الدكتور«لازم نعرف شو سبب حالتك،
ريّح حالك عالصّوفا وخبّرني عن مشكلتك.»
قلو أبو العبد «لا، لا ما بقدر، أم العبد مانعتني اطلع على
الكنبايات!»

Abou Abed visited a prominent psychiatrist.
"Doctor, I have a major problem. I keep imagining that I am a large, white,
mountain dog and sometimes I bark. I don't know what to do about it!"
"Ok, don't worry, we'll find out the cause.
Please lie down on the couch and tell me all about your problem."
Abou Abed suddenly panicked. "No, no doctor, Em Abed doesn't allow me
to jump on the couch!"

سافر أبو العبد على نيويورك تيشارك بمؤتمر حول التغذية. قالت أخصّائية التغذية «الأكل اللي مناكلو يمكن يقتلنا! اللحم الأحمر مئذي كتير، والخضار بتكون ملوثة أغلب الوقت، وما ننسى الجراثيم بمي الشرب. بس في شي مناكلو هوّ الأخطر وكتار منّا بياكلو، حدا بيعرف الأكل السّام يلي عم عم بحكي عنّو؟» رفع أبو العبد أيدو وقال بصوت عالي «كاتو العرس!»

Abou Abed traveled to New York to attend a conference about nutrition. "The food we eat can kill us! Red meat is very harmful and vegetables are often polluted, not to mention the germs in our drinking water. But, there is one particular food that is the most dangerous of them all. Does anyone here know which toxic food I am referring to?" asked the dietician. Abou Abed raised his hand and shouted out, "Wedding cake!"

فات أبو العبد على قهوة وديني تنيناتون مربّطين. سألو أبو صطيف «شو صار لدينيك؟» ردّ أبو العبد «أم العبد طلعت عالجبل، واضطريت أكوي قميصي، لما دقّ التلفون، جيت عمرّد بسرعة وحطيت المكواية على ديتي.» قلو أبو صطيف، «طيّب حرقت أول ديني، والتانية شو صرلا؟»
ردّ أبو العبد «إيه ما بدّي تلفن للدكتور؟»

Abou Abed walks into a cafe with both of his ears bandaged. "What happened to your ears?" asked Abou Steif. "Em Abed was away in the mountains, so I was forced to iron my own shirt! When the phone rang, I accidentally held the iron to my ear," answered Abou Abed. "That explains one ear, but what happened to your other ear?" asked Abou Steif. Abou Abed replied, "Well, I had to call the doctor, didn't I?"

أبو العبد وتنين من اصحابو عمبقدمو على الشرطة ليتوظفو. قام الضابط. عطاهن كل واحد مسدس وقلهن «بدي شوف اخلاصكن وكيف رح تنفذو هل أوامر، بدّي من كل واحد منكن يروح يقتل مرتو ويرجع». أول واحد دغري رفض، وقلّ. التاني حمل المسدس وضهر، رجع بعد ساعة وقلو للضابط «سيدنا ما قدرت نفذ». بعد ساعتين رجع أبو العبد وقال للضابط «بدي أعرف مين حطلّي رصاص فاضي، اضطريت اقتلها خنق!»

Abou Abed and two of his friends decided to answer a police recruitment ad. When they arrived for the interview, the police officer told the recruits that he intended to test their commitment - each one had to go home and shoot his wife. He then gave each person a gun. The first recruit refused outright and said that he couldn't kill his wife. The second recruit went home, but came back an hour later saying that he couldn't go through with it. Then, it was Abou Abed's turn. He went home and returned a couple of hours later angry and sweating, "Which idiot put fake bullets in my gun?" shouted Abou Abed. "I had to kill her with my bare hands!"

أبو العبد عند الحلاق عم بقص شعرو، قلو للحلاق «سمعت آخر تصريح لأوباما؟»
جاوبو الحلاق «إذا بتريد أبو العبد ممنوع الحكي بالسياسة بهالمحل.» بعد شوي
قلو أبو العبد «قدي سعر اليورو اليوم؟» جاوبو الحلاق «أبو العبد لو سمحت ممنوع
الحكي بالإقتصاد بهالمحل». رجع قلو أبو العبد «طيب، سمعت بالزلزال اللي
ضرب مكسيكو مبارح؟» قلو الحلاق «أبو العبد عمول معروف، ممنوع الحكي
بالكوارث بهالمحل». آخر شي قلو أبو العبد «طيب فينا نحكي سكس؟» جاوبو
الحلاق «طبعاً». قام فلّ أبو العبد وقلو «ايه، فيك وبهالمحل».

One day Abou Abed visited his barber for a haircut. "Did you hear what
Obama said today?" he asked the barber. "Please Abou Abed, we don't
want to hear any politics," pleaded the barber. A few minutes later, Abou
Abed asked "How is the euro doing today?" The barber replied, "Please,
we don't want any talk about the economy in here." After a while, Abou
Abed asked the barber "Did you hear about the earthquake in Mexico?"
The barber suddenly became angry. "Please Abou Abed, let's not talk
of disasters in here!" "Well can we at least talk about sex?" insisted
Abou Abed. "Yes, of course," replied the barber. "Well f... you and your
barbershop!" shouted Abou Abed, before angrily storming out.

كان أبو العبد عم بيساير مرا حلوي بحفلة، قلا أنو هوي ساحر قوي، وبدو يفرجيا شطارتو ببيتو. قبلت المرا العزيمة، وراحت معو عالبيت وقالتلو «فرجيني سحرك يا أبو العبد». قلا «بسيطة، بتجي معي عالبيت، بتقضي معي الليلة، وتاني يوم بخفيكي!»

Abou Abed was trying to charm a pretty lady at a party. He told her that he was an excellent magician and wanted to show her some of his tricks at home. The lady accepted the invitation, and went home with him.

"So Abou Abed, show me what you can do!" she said.

"It's simple. I take you home, you stay the night, and the next day, I'll make you disappear!" explained Abou Abed.

أبو العبد عم يحلق بالراديو تبعو،
شافو أبو صطيف وسألو «شو بيك يا أبو العبد؟»
جاوب أبو العبد «مش عم بعرف شو يعني AM وFM.»
قلو أبو صطيف «ولو يا ذكي، FM يعني في موسيقى،
وAM يعني أفيش موسيقى.»

Abou Abed was sitting at home staring at his radio.
Abou Steif comes in and asks him, "What on earth are you doing?"
"I don't understand. What does AM and FM mean?" replied Abou Abed.
"You fool!" replied Abou Steif,
"FM means '*Fi Musi'a*'
and AM means '*Afish Musi'a*'."

أبو العبد تعلم بالمدرسة الفرنسي، ما علّمو الإنكليزي.
فراح عالمركز البريطاني ليدرس إنكليزي. عجبتو المعلمة،
فكتبلها رسالة إعجاب «آي سينك آي أم فالينغ إن لوف ويز يو،
دو يو سينك وي كان كراك كراك زيس إيفنغ؟»
«Never!!» فردّت علي
جاوبا أبو العبد «!Super! Disons neuve heure, neuve heure et demie»

At school, Abou Abed learnt French, but never English.

So, last year he decided to take an English course at a language school.

He soon developed a crush on the English teacher

and decided to send her a note,

"*I sink aya am foling in love wiziou. Dou you sink it is possible crak crak wiziou this ivining?*"

She sends him back a note "Never!!"

Abou Abed replied, "*Super! Disons neuve heure, neuve heure et demie!*"

فات أبو العبد عالصيدلية وسأل
«عندك شي دوا للصراصير؟»
ردّ علي الفرمشاني
«سلامتون، شو مشكلتون؟»

One morning, Abou Abed went to his local pharmacy.
"Do you have anything for cockroaches?"
he asked the man behind the counter.
"Why, what's wrong with them?"
enquired the pharmacist.

كان أبو العبد على الطيارة،
عيّط للمضيفة وقلا أنو ديني عم يوجعو،
راحت وجابتلو علكة.
هوي ونازل من الطيارة راح عند المضيفة وقلا «بتشكّرك على
العلكة، كتير ريّحتني،
بس بدّي عزبك، فيكي تقيليلي كيف بشيلا من ديني؟»

During his flight to Paris,
Abou Abed complained to an attendant that his ears were hurting him.
So, the hostess offered him some chewing gum.
At the end of the trip, Abou Abed says to her, "Thank you very much for
the gum. It helped me a lot. But, how am I supposed to take it out
of my ears?"

إجا أبو العبد معصّب،
إلو شهر عم بجرّب يبيع سيّارتو ‹رينو 5›، وما حدا عم يشتريا،
قلّو أبو صطيف «مين بعد بيشتري ‹رينو 5› هل أيّام؟»
أنا محلّك بشيل عنّا إسما وبحطّ إسم ‹مرسيدس›.
بعد شهرين، التقا في أبو صطيف وسألو «شو انشالله توفقت بالبيعة؟»
ردّ أبو العبد «أكيد لأ يا زلمي،
حدن عنده ‹مرسيدس› و بقوم بيبيعها!»

Abou Abed decided to sell his car.
"It has been a whole month since I've been trying to sell my Renault 5,
and I've had no luck!"
Abou Steif replies, "Who would buy a Renault 5 these days?
If I were you, I'd replace the Renault sign with a Mercedes sign
and then offer it up for sale."
Two months later, Abou Steif asks Abou Abed if he managed to sell his car.
"No, of course not, only an idiot would sell a Mercedes," Abou Abed replied.

إجت أم العبد معصبة ،
«يا أبو العبد، لازم تشحط هالشوفور، ما بيعرف يسوق،
كان قتلني أربع مرّات هالجمعة».
قلا أبو العبد «ما علي أم العبد، عطي بعد فرصة واحدة!»

Em Abed asks Abou Abed to fire their chauffeur for being a crazy driver.
"He almost killed me four times this week because of his bad driving!" she
says. "It's alright dear, just give him one more chance!"
replies Abou Abed.

راح أبو العبد مع إبنو عبد عالمخفر ليبلّغ أنّو مضيّع مرته من أسبوعين، سألو الشّرطي «شُو مواصفات مرتك؟»

ردّ أبو العبد «طويلة، شُقرا، أمورة، وعيونها خضر.»

استغرب عبد وقلو «بابا... بابا... هيدي مش مواصفات الماما.»

قلو أبو العبد «سكوت، بركي بيجيبولنا وحدة أحلى!»

Abou Abed's wife went missing so he went to the police station
to ask them to find her.

The police asked for a description of Em Abed.

"She's tall, blonde, with green eyes," explains Abou Abed.

His son interrupts him. "*Baba*, what are you saying,
mama doesn't look anything like that?"

Abou Abed shuts him up saying, "Shhh! They might find us someone
better looking than your *mama!*"

أبو العبد شايف حالو عم بخبّر أبو صطيف عن دروسو الخصوصيّة. قام تضحّك أبو صطيف. فقلو أبو العبد «بتعرف مين بيكون غراهام بيل؟» هزّ أبو صطيف براسو. «هو اللي اخترع التلفون سنة 1876. لو كنت عم تاخد دروس متلي كنت عرفتو.» تاني يوم سأل أبو العبد أبو صطيف «بتعرف مين بيكون ألكسندر دوماس؟» كمان هزّ أبو صطيف براسو. «هو اللي كتب «الفرسان الثلاثة». لو كنت عم تاخد دروس متلي كنت عرفتو.»

تالت يوم سأل أبو العبد أبو صطيف «بتعرف مين بيكون جان جاك روسو؟» هزّ أبو صطيف براسو. «هو اللي كتب «اعترافات». لو كنت عم تاخد دروس متلي كنت عرفتو.» عصّب أبو صطيف وقلو «بتعرف مين بيكون أبو وليد الزرنباوي؟» قلو أبو العبد «لأ ما بعرفو.» قام ردّ أبو صطيف «هو اللي عمب نام مع مرتك كل ليلة. لو بتوقّف تاخد هل دروس كنت عرفتو!»

Abou Abed was telling Abou Steif about the evening courses he'd been taking. "Bahhh," replies Abou Steif unimpressed. So Abou Abed asked him, "Fine, do you know who Graham Bell is?" Abou Steif shook his head. "He invented the telephone in 1876. If you attended night courses you would've known this," boasted Abou Abed. "Do you know who Alexandre Dumas is?" "No," replied Abou Steif. "He's the famous author of 'The Three Musketeers'. If you took night courses, you would have learnt this," bragged Abou Abed. "Do you know who Jean Jacques Rousseau is?" Abou Steif replied, "No." "He is the author of 'Confessions'. If you took night courses, you would've known this," boasted Abou Abed. Abou Steif got irritated and said, "And you, do you know who Abou Walid Al-Zernbewi is?" "No," replied Abou Abed. "He's the guy who's sleeping with Em Abed. If you stop taking night courses, you would know this!"

قلو أبو صطيف لأبو العبد
«يا زلمي، مش عيب عليك مبارح عشيّة تبوس أم العبد
عالبلكون قدام كل الناس؟!»
رد أبو العبد
«مبارح؟ بحلفلك مش أنا، بقيت بالقهوة لنصّ الليّل،
مش مصدّقني سأل الشباب اللي كانو سهرانين معي!»

Abou Steif says to Abou Abed,
"How could you kiss Em Abed yesterday evening
on your balcony in front of everyone?"
Abou Abed replied, "It wasn't me, I swear,
I was at the coffee shop yesterday evening.
Ask my friends who were there too if you don't believe me!"

كان أبو العبد مسرع بالسيارة، فلحقتو سيارة الشّرطة. لمّا لاقى أنو ما رح يقدر يهرب، وقف عاليمين. نزل الشّرطي من السيارة وقلو «ليك، قريباً بيخلص دوامي، رح كون منيح معك وفلتك إذا بتعطيني سبب مقنع ليش كنت مسرع.» فكّر أبو العبد شوي وقلو «هربت أم العبد من أسبوع مع شرطي، ولما شفتك لاحقني خفت تكون أنت هو، وبدّك تردّلي ياها.»

A police officer was chasing Abou Abed's speeding car down the highway. At first, Abou Abed didn't slow down but he eventually realized he couldn't escape and decided to pull over.

The policeman approached the car and said, "Look, It's been a long day and my tour of duty is almost over. So, if you can give me a good explanation for your speeding, I'll let you go." Abou Abed thought for a few seconds and then said, "Em Abed ran away with a cop about a week ago and I was scared you might be that officer trying to give her back to me."

كان أبو العبد مارق على جسر،
شاف رجّال واقع بالميّ وعم بيصرّخ بالفرنسي
«Au secours, Au secours!»
قلو أبو العبد «بدل ما تضيّع وقتك وتتعلم الفرنسي،
ما كان أزبطلك تتعلم السباحة؟»

Abou Abed was crossing a bridge
when he noticed a man in the water.
The man was obviously drowning and he was yelling in
French, "Au secours! Au secours!"
Abou Abed leaned over the rails and yelled at him,
"Instead of wasting your time learning French,
you should have learnt how to swim!"

يوم الأحد عبكرا، وعي أبو العبد وقال لمرتو
«اليوم أحد، وبدّي أنبسط بالنهار، اشتريت 3 بطاقات سينما.»
استغربت أم العبد
«ليش 3 بطاقات؟»
ردّ أبو العبد
«لإلك ولأمّك ولبيّك!»

One Sunday morning, Abou Abed wakes up and tells Em Abed,
"Today is Sunday and I want to really enjoy my day off.
So here are three movies tickets that I bought."
Em Abed is puzzled and asks,
"Why three?"
Abou Abed replies,
"They're for you and your parents!"

أم العبد هديتو لأبو العبد بعيد ميلادو لعبة تركيب أحجية،
فرح فيها وأخذها على بيتو بالجبل وبقي سنتين عمبيركبها.
بهالفترة كانو أهلو ما سمعو عنو شي ومفكرين صرلو شي.
حتى بيوم من الأيام دق الباب بييروت، فتحتلو أم العبد وقالت
«وينك يا زلمي، صرلك سنتين ما بينت، افتكرناك متت.» ردّ أبو
العبد مبسوط «حليتها... حليتها بس بسنتين مع أنو مكتوب
عالحلبة من تلات لخمس سنين!»

Em Abed bought Abou Abed a jigsaw puzzle for his birthday.
He was so excited about his gift that he took off for a weekend in the
mountains to work on the puzzle. For the next two years, his family did
not hear a word from him, so they assumed that he had an accident and
died. Then one day he appeared out of the blue. "I did it, I did it!" he shouted
cheerfully entering the house. "Where have you been all this time, we thought
you were dead!" yelled Em Abed. "I finished the puzzle. On the box
it said '3-5 years' but I finished it in 2!"

أبو العبد سرلو فترة على علاقة مع ست إيطالية. بليلة قالتلو السّت أنّها حامل. ليحافظ على سمعتو وزواجو دفعلها لترجع على إيطاليا وتخلّف بالسّرّ. ووعدها إذا بتضلّ هونيك بأمّن مصروف الولد ليصير عمرو ١٨. وقلها «بس تولدي بعتيلي بوست كارد مكتوب عليه «سباغيتي»، تبلّش أبعتلك مصاري.» بعد ٩ أشهر بيوصل لأبو العبد بوست كارد من إيطاليا مكتوب عليه «سباغيتي، سباغيتي، سباغيتي، سباغيتي، تنين مع هوتة دوغ وتنين بلا هوتة دوغ. وبعتلي صلصة زيادة.» اصفرّ وجّ أبو العبد وغاب عن الوعي.

For several years, Abou Abed had an affair with an Italian woman. One night, she told him that she was pregnant. Not wanting to ruin his reputation or his marriage, he paid her a large sum of money to return to Italy and secretly have the child. If she remained in Italy to raise the child, he promised her child support until the child turned 18. He told her to send him a postcard, and write 'Spaghetti' on the back once the child was born. He would then arrange for the child support payments to begin. About 9 months later, he receives a postcard with a picture of Rome. He turned it round and read 'Spaghetti, spaghetti, spaghetti, spaghetti, two with meatballs, two without. Please send extra sauce.' Abou Abed turned pale and fainted.

خسر أبو العبد كلّ مصرياتو بالقمار.
هو وماشي حدّ مبنى البلدية شاف رئيس البلدية وسألو
«لمين هيدي البناية؟!»
قلو «لكل أهل البسطة.»
قلو أبو العبد «فإذاً بدّي بيع حصتي!»

One night, Abou Abed gambled away all of his money.
So, the next day he went to the municipality to talk with the Mayor.
"Mayor, who actually owns this building?" asked Abou Abed.
"It belongs to all the people of Basta," the Mayor replied.
"In that case, I would like to sell my share!"

طلب أبو العبد بيتزا،
سألو الفرّان «بدّك ياني قطّعلك ياها 6 قطع أو 12؟»
ردّ أبو العبد «6 قطع أكيد،
مين في ياكل 12؟»

One day, Abou Abed went to his local bakery and ordered a pizza.
The salesperson at the counter asked him,
"Would you prefer your pizza to be cut in 6 or 12 slices?"
Abou Abed immediately replied,
"*Laaa*, 6 please! I couldn't possibly eat 12 slices!"

لاحظ عبد أنو في براس بيّو كم شَعرة شايبة ظاهرين،
سألو «بابا؟ لي عندك شَعر أبيض؟»
قلو أبو العبد «كلما بتعمل أنت شي غلط وبتعصّبني،
بتبيّض شَعرة براسي.»
فكّر الصبي بالموضوع شْوي ورجع سأل
«طيب ليش كل شَعرات ستّي بيض؟»

Abed noticed that his father had several strands of white hair sticking out
from his mostly dark-haired head.
He looked at his father and inquisitively asked,
"*Baba*, why are some of your hairs white?"
Abou Abed replied, "Well, every time you do something wrong and make
me mad, one of my hairs turns white."
The son thought about this revelation for a long while and then said,
"*Baba*, how come all of *teta's* hairs are white then?"

سأل أبو العبد رجّال عالطريق

«قدّي الساعة من فضلك؟»

جاوبو «الساعة أربعة وربع»،

استغرب أبو العبد وقال «شي غريب، صرت سائل هالسؤال

عشرين مرّة اليوم،

وكل واحد بيعطيني جواب شكل!»

Abou Abed asked someone on the road,

"Excuse me, what time is it right now?"

"It's 4:15," came the reply.

Very much confused, Abou Abed added,

"You know, it's the weirdest thing, I've asked that question about twenty

times today, and every time someone gives me a different answer!"

كان أبو العبد مع صاحبو أبو صطيف بالسيارة،
طلب منّو أبو صطيف يشْفلو إذا الإشارة عم بتضوي.
مدّ أبو العبد راسو من الشّباك وقلو
«إي، لأ، إي، لأ، إي، لأ...»

Abou Steif was driving in his car with Abou Abed.
He asked Abou Abed to stick his head out the window and check if the
blinker was working properly.
So, Abou Abed stuck his head out and said,
"Yes, no, yes, no, yes... "

راح أبو العبد ليشْتري تلفزيون ملوّن لأوّل مرّة،
وصل عأوّل محل وسأل «عندك تلفزيونات ملوّنة؟»
جاوبو البياع «أكيد»
فقلو أبو العبد «طيب، بدي عزبك بواحد أخضر.»

Abou Abed went to buy his first color television.

He strolled into the electronics shop and asked,

"Do you sell color TV's?"

"Of course we do," the salesperson replied.

So Abou Abed says, "OK, I want to buy a green one."

رجع أبو العبد من شغلو وشاف أم العبد مع أبو صطيف بالتخت.
عصّب وركض عالمطبخ ورجع حامل سكين «بدي أقتلكن
تنيناتكون.» ركضت علي أم العبد «روق يا أبو العبد، ما تتسرّع،
هيدي مزحة، أنت قدام الكاميرا الخفية.»
عصّب أبو العبد وقال «خلصونا بقا، هيدي تالت مرا هالأسبوع
بطلع عالكاميرا الخفية!»

Abou Abed arrives home from work and finds Em Abed and Abou Steif in
bed together. Abou Abed gets very angry and storms into the kitchen
to fetch a large knife. "I'm going to kill the both of you," he shouts waving
the knife about his head. Shaking with fear, Em Abed cries out,
"Calm down Abou Abed, don't kill us! This is a big joke,
you are on candid camera."
Abou Abed then yells out, "Enough of this nonsense, this is the third time
this week that I've been on candid camera!"

اشترى أبو العبد سيارة وأخد أم العبد مشوار. لمّا وصلو عأول تقاطع مرق عالضو الأحمر بسرعة. سألتو أم العبد «شو عمتعمل؟ بدك تقتلنا؟» قلا «روقي، هيك بيسوق أبو صطيف.» عالتقاطع التاني، كمان مرق عالضو الأحمر، صرخت في أم العبد «شو عميصرلك، هي تاني مرة بتمرق عالضو الأحمر»، قلا «مش شغلك، عمبعمل متل ما بيسوق أبو صطيف.» عالتقاطع التالت، وقف أبو العبد عالضو الأخضر، جنّت أم العبد وقالتلو «طيب هلأ ليش وقفت عالضو الأخضر يا حمار؟» جاوبا «يا غبية، يمكن يكون أبو صطيف جايي من تاني طريق.»

Abou Abed buys a new car and takes Em Abed for a drive. At the first crossroads, he speeds through a red light. Em Abed asks Abou Abed, "What are you doing, are you trying to get us killed?" Abou Abed replies, "Be quiet, this is the way Abou Steif drives." At the second crossroads, Abou Abed again speeds through a red light. This time, Em Abed gets very angry and shouts, "What are you doing, you're crazy, you've driven through another set of red lights." Abou Abed replies, "This is none of your business, I am only copying the way Abou Steif drives". At the third crossroads, Abou Abed stops at a green light. Em Abed is furious by now, "Why are you stopping at the green light, you idiot?" Abou Abed replies, "You fool, just in case Abou Steif is driving the other way."

صار عمر أبو العبد ١٠٠ سنة، وإجا صحفي تيقابلو، سألو
«أبو العبد، منعرف أنك رمز الرجولة اللبنانيّة،
بس كيف بعدك بصحتك؟»
قلو أبو العبد «بعمل سيكس كل يوم.»
فسألو «شو اللي بتطلبو من المرا بهالعمر؟»
اضحّك أبو العبد ورّد :«نبض!»

Abou Abed turned 100 years old and a reporter
was sent to interview him.
"Abou Abed, we all know that you are a symbol of Lebanese virility,
but how do you keep it up?" asked the reporter.
"My recipe is to make love as often as possible."
"And what do you look for in women at your age?" enquired the reporter.
"A beating pulse!" laughed Abou Abed.

أبو العبد عمل حادث قوي وفيت سنتين كوما. بس قام لقى أمّ العبد حدّه بالمستشفى وقلها «ما عم صدّق أنت هون معي، صرلك ناترتيني سنتين لأوعى! لما صار معي الحادث كنت معي، ولما فلست وما بقي معي مصاري لنربّي الأولاد كنت معي، ولما كسرت اجري كنت معي.» تأسّرت أمّ العبد ودمّعت. كمّل أبو العبد «حتى لما توفو بيّي وأمّي كنت معي.» ردّت أمّ العبد «أكيد حبيبي ،مين إلي غيرك؟»«أيه روحي حبيبتي أنتي طالق لأنو أنحس من هيك وجّ ما في.»

Abou Abed had a severe car accident and fell into a coma for two years. When he woke up, he found Em Abed next to him and said, "I can't believe that you're here with me in the hospital. For two years you have waited for me to wake up. When I had the accident, you were at my side, when I went bankrupt and had no money left to raise the kids, you never left my side, and when I broke my leg you were there for me." Em Abed was so overwhelmed that she had tears in her eyes. Abou Abed continued, "Even when my father and mother died, you were with me." Em Abed replied, "Of course *habibi*, if I didn't stand by your side, then who would?" "That's it, I want a divorce immediately!" Abou Abed said. "Look at all the bad luck you have brought me over the years."

كان أبو العبد مريض، فراح لعند الحكيم ليفحصو.
بعد الفحص، عيّط الحكيم لأمّ العبد ليطمّنا
أنو أبو العبد منيح بس لازمو رواق،
و قلّها «هول شْويّت حبوب منومة.»
سألتو أم العبد «أيمتا بعطي ياهون؟»
قلّها الحكيم «لأ، ما عم تفهمي، هول وصفتون لإلِك!»

Abou Abed isn't feeling well, so he goes to the doctor for a checkup.
After the examination, the doctor calls in Em Abed to tell her that there
is nothing seriously wrong with Abou Abed but that he just
needs some peace and quiet.
Then the doctor says, "Here are some sleeping pills."
"When should I give them to him?" Em Abed asks.
The doctor answers, "No, you don't understand, they are for YOU!"

نزلت أمّ العبد عالدكان تشتري غراض، سمعت أبو العبد عم بيصرخ لا عن البلكون «أم عبد، تعي هلأ بسرعة»، قالتلو «مش شايفني عم بشتري غراض؟»

«تركي كل شي وتعي، ربحت مليون دولار باللوتو.»

ركضت أم العبد راجعة عالبيت، فضربتا سيارة هيّ وقاطعة الطريق. شافا أبو العبد، ضحك وقال «أخ شو حلو حظي ، صار أحسن وأحسن!»

Em Abed went across the road to buy some groceries,
when she heard Abou Abed screaming from the balcony,
"Em Abed, Em Abed, come right away."
"Can't you see I'm getting the groceries," she screamed back.
"Leave everything and come, I just won a million dollars in the lotto!"
So Em Abed hurriedly dropped everything and as she was crossing the
road, she got hit by a car. Abou Abed stared, then laughed and said,
"My luck just keeps getting better!"

قلا عبد لأمّو

«أنا وجايي بالباص مع بابا، قلي لأوقف وقعّد مرا محلّي».

قالتلو أم العبد

«برافو عليك يا مزوق، لازم عطول تسمع كلمة بيّك».

فقلا عبد «بس كنت قاعد بحرج بيّي!»

Abed came home one day and told his mum,

"*Mama*, when I was on the bus today,

baba told me to get up and give my seat to a lady."

Em Abed replied,

"*Bravo*, that's kind of you, you should always listen to your father."

Abed looked confused and then replied, "But, I was sitting on his lap!"

فتح أبو العبد القاموس، ونبّش على كلمة «قاموس»،
لاقى الجواب «القاموس هو الشّي اللي بين إيديك يا غبي»،
استغرب ونبّش على كلمة «غبي»
لاقى الجواب «هيدا إنت كمان؟!»

Abou Abed was searching for the meaning
of the word 'Dictionary' in his dictionary.
Finally, he found the following,
'Dictionary is the thing you are holding, stupid.'
Wondering what the definition of 'Stupid' could be,
he searched for the word in his dictionary and found,
'Is that you again?'

نروي فيها نكات أبو عبد للتّرفيه عن أنفسنا في تلك الحالة المتوتّرة. وقد اشتهر زوجي بمجموعة نكاته الواسعة وسرده المسهب. ومنذ بضع سنوات، بدأت أسجّل ما أذكره من هذه النكات، وخطرت لي فكرة نشر كتاب أقدّم فيه أبرز شخصيّة فكاهيّة إلى جمهور لبنانيّ واسع.

قد ينتقد بعضكم اختياري للنكات، ويخيب ظنّه لعدم رؤية نكتته المفضّلة في الكتاب. ولكن من يعرف شخصيّة أبو عبد يعلم أنّ أفضل نكاته إباحيّة من العيار الثقيل، ولا يمكنني كتابتها ونشرها على الورق.

أعتقد أنّ أبو عبد ينتمي إلى حقبة مثاليّة عابرة في لبنان لم يواجه فيها المواطن اللبنانيّ مشاكل كبرى، ولذلك كان قلقه الأكبر كيفيّة التمتّع بوقته مع الأصدقاء.

يمثّل أبو العبد الرجل اللبنانيّ العاديّ الّذي بالرّغم مع كلّ سيّئاته، تظهر روعته أيضاً– وهي هنا روح الفكاهة الفريدة. وتجدر الإشارة هنا أنّ بالرغم من فكاهيّة أبو عبد ، لطالما تساءلت عن إمكانيّة بروزه كبطل الطبقة العاملة، رغم شخصيّته المتحيّزة الذكوريّة.

أين هو الآن؟ يبدو أنّ أبو العبد أزليّ ويعايش العصور، ويرافق كلّ الأجيال اللبنانيّة. قد لا تكون شخصيّته مثاليّة، لكن ما دامت النكات تتوالى، فما الفرق؟ فلنواصل البحث وأخبروني عندما تجدونه، أودّ سماع قصصه منه.

سابينا، بيروت، كانون الأول ٢٠٠٩

المقدمة

صُدم كثيرٌ من اللبنانيّن عندما نشوَ كتاب نكات أبو عبد سنة ٢٠٠٨. وقد تردّد عليّ سؤالُ: لماذا لم يفكّر أحدٌ بنشر كتابٍ كهذا سابقاً؟ حقّق كتاب أبو عبد نجاحاً باهراً ممّا دفعني إلى جمع وتأليف هذا الجزء الثّاني.

وهذه المرّة يبرز أبو عبد من خلال رسومات دانييل جورج.

من هو أبو عبد؟ هذه مقدّمة صغيرة: أبوعبد، مع طربوشه الأحمر وشاربيه الكبيرين، اللذّين يشكّلان رمزا لرجولته، من أبرز الشخصيّات الفكاهيّة المعروفة في لبنان. تطوّر من كونه نسج الخيال إلى شخصيّة مهمّة تتبوّأ مئات النكات. يقضي وقته مع صديقه أبو صطيف في مقهى بيروتيّ حيث يلعبان الورق وطاولة النرد. حول فناجين لا تحصى من الشاي، يتبادل أبو صطيف وأبو عبد قصصًا مضخّمة تدور حول مآثرهما الجنسيّة. ولسوء حالته الماديّة، يلجأ أبوعبد دومًا إلى ورق الشّدة واليانصيب.

أبو عبد متزوّج من أمّ عبد ولديهما ابنٌ بكر يُدعى عبد. يتحمّل الإثنان تبعة مزحات أبو عبد لكنّهما يثوران من تجاوز حدّه . يدفعنا أبو عبدَ دائمًا إلى التساؤل عن مهنته وميوله الجنسيّة، إذ يبدو وكأنّه لا يعمل ويرضى بكّل ما يتسّنى له.

أسرتني شخصيّة أبو عبد منذ سنوات عديدة، تحديداً خلال الحرب الأهليّة اللبنانيّة، التي أرغمت العديد منّا على ملازمة المنزل لفتراتٍ طويلة. كنّا في معظم الأوقات نقضي الأمسيات مع الأقارب والجيران،

الى أبو تارا و أبو ويليم

بما أنّ أبو عبد ينتمي الى المجتمع اللبنانيّ جزء من عائدات هذا الكتاب ستخصّص
لجمعيّة CIFA (Centre d'Insertion pour la Formation et l'Activité) الخيريّة اللبنانيّة
لدعم المشاريع الإنمائيّة في أرجاء لبنان.

turningpoint
BOOKS

الطابق 15، بناية كونكورد، شارع دونان، فردان، بيروت، لبنان

ص.ب. 6613-14

هاتف: 100 752 1 961+

فاكس: 555 748 1 961+

www.tpbooksonline.com

الطبعة الأولى: كانون الأول 2009

ISBN: 978-9953-0-1583-5

طباعة: **dots**

كتاب نكات أبو عبد ②

The Abou Abed Joke Book ②

جمعتها: سابينا محفوظ

رسوم: دانييل جورج

تنقيح: عبد المولى، طارق بلوط، كلود كرم

تصميم: مايا طويل